265
Vintage
Botanical
Illustrations

EDITIONS Vault

Download your files

This 2019 offering from Vault Editions is a brilliantly curated resource of copyright-free vintage botanical illustrations. With artwork from acclaimed botanical illustrators such as Hoola van Nooten, George Worthington Smith and Nicholas Edward Brown, this pictorial archive features a diverse range of species including lush tropical flowers, fruits and foliage, carnivorous plants, exotic fungi through to masterfully rendered perennials, roses, trees, classic English garden varietals and more.

To access the download page for all your files please go to the below web address and enter your unique password and follow the prompts.

www.vaulteditions.com/vbi
Password: xsew6789er3

Bibliographical note
This book is a new work created by Avenue House Press Pty Ltd.

ISBN: 978-1-925968-04-0

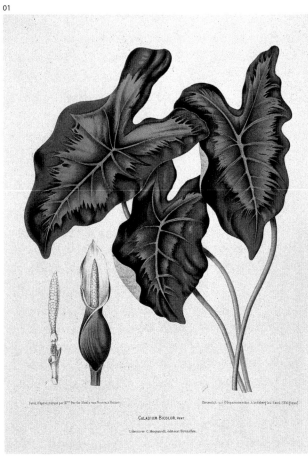

CALADIUM BICOLOR, Vent

TRADESCANTIA DISCOLOR

AMHERSTIA NOBILIS WALL.

FLORES JAMBOSAE DOMESTICAE, Rumph

Fig.01 Caladium bicolour (Aiton) Vent.

Fig.02 Spiderwort (Tradescantia discolor).

Fig.03 Amherstia Nobilis Wall.

Fig.04 Flores Jambosae Domesticae.

Peint d'après nature par Mme Berthe Hoola van Nooten à Batavia. Chromolith par P. Depannemaeker à Ledeberg-lez-Gand. (Belgique).

ELETTARIA SPECIOSA

Librairie C. Muquardt éditeur Bruxelles.

Fig.05 Elettaria Speciosa.

06

07

08

09

Fig.06 Croton (Codiaeum variegatum (L.) Blume).

Fig.07 Pride-of-India, queen flower or pyinma (Lagerstroemia speciosa (L.) Pers.).

Fig.08 A fig plant (Ficus carica var.).

Fig.09 An orchid (Cattleya guttata).

ARTOCARPUS.

The Bread Fruit Tree.

London, Published as the Act directs, Sept.3.1796. by J.Wilkes.

Fig.10 A Bread Fruit Tree.

VINTAGE BOTANICAL ILLUSTRATION

Peint d'après nature par Mᵐᵉ Berthe Hoola van Nooten à Batavia.

Chromolith par P. Depannemaeker, à Ledeberg-lez-Gand. [Belgique].

STERCULIA NOBILIS. SMITH.-

Librairie C. Muquardt, éditeur, Bruxelles.

Fig.06 Sterculia nobilis Smith.

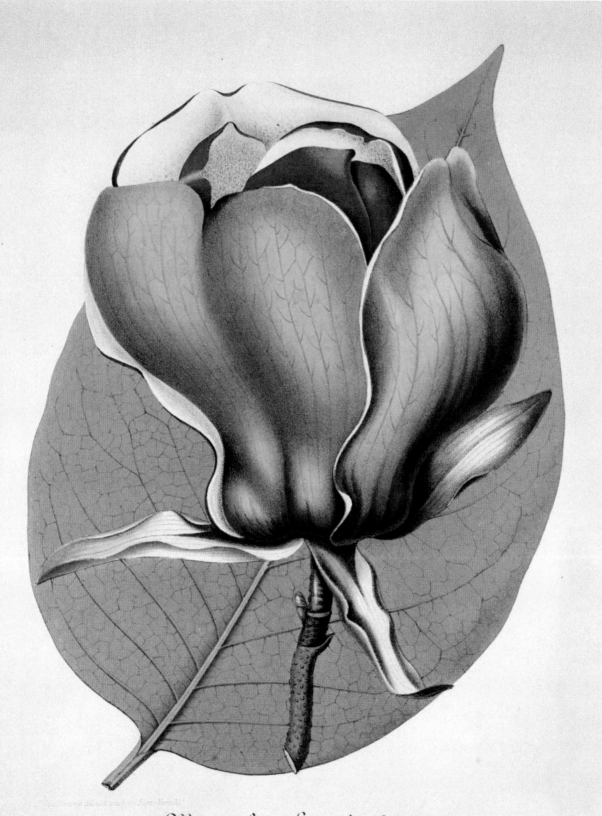

Magnolia Lenné (hybride).
Italie (Semis) _ Plein air.

L. Verschaffelt publ.

Fig.12 Magnolia Lenne.

13

14

15

16

Fig.13 Braddick's American peach (Prunus persica cv.).

Fig.14 Almond plant (Prunus dulcis).

Fig.15 Two strawberry plants.

Fig.16 Two plums (Prunus cultivars).

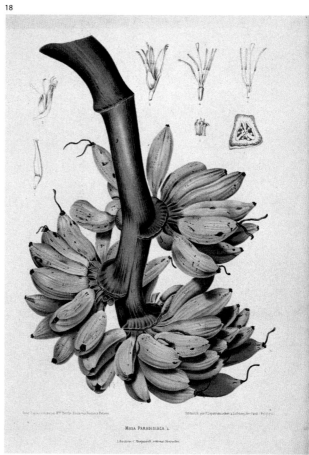

Fig.17 Breadfruit (Artocarpus altilis).

Fig.18 Plantain banana (Musa paradisiaca L.).

Fig.19 Two pears (Pyrus cultivars).

Fig.20 Cashew nut or acajou (Anacardium occidentale L.).

21

22

23

24

Fig.21 Melon (Cucumis melo).

Fig.22 Lepisanthes.

Fig.23 Peach plant (Prunus persica).

Fig.24 Pear (Pyrus communis cv.).

25

CITRUS MEDICA LIMON *Aurantiata Major*

Lima grossa dolce di Spagna

26

CITRUS SARCODACTYLIS Hort. Boe.

27

28

CITRUS DECUMANA

Fig.25 Citron (Citrus medica L.).

Fig.26 Citrus sarcodactylis Hort.

Fig.27 A lemon plant (Citrus japonica).

Fig.28 Pummelo or Pamplemousse.

29

30

31

32

Fig.29 Langsat (Lansium domesticum Corr. Serr.).

Fig.30 Custard apple (Annona triloba).

Fig.31 Ketaki (Pandanus tectorius Sol. ex Parkinson).

Fig.32 Ketaki (Pandanus tectorius Sol. ex Parkinson).

33

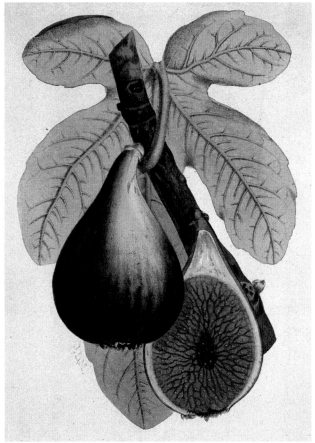

34

35

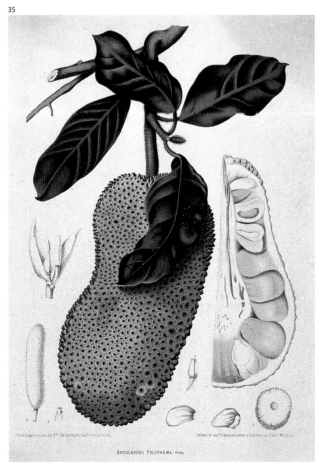

ARTOCARPUS POLYPHEMA. Pers.

36

MUSA COCCINEA Andr.

Fig.33 A fig plant (Ficus carica).   Fig.34 The flat peach of China.   Fig.35 Champedak (Artocarpus polyphema Pers.).   Fig.36 Banana (Musa coccinea Andr.).

37

38

39

40

Fig.37 Rose apple (Syzygium jambos (L.) Alston).

Fig.38 Four cultivars of pear (Pyrus communis cv.).

Fig.39 Two cultivars of mango (Mangifera indica cv.).

Fig.40 Four cultivars of pear (Pyrus communis cv.).

41

1.The Cocoa Fruit as it grows upon the Tree. 2. A Section of the same to shew the Formation of the Nut. 3. A Section of the Nut to shew the Kernel. 4. The perfect Kernel extracted.

42

NEPHELIUM LAPPACEUM.

43

THEOBROMA CACAO.

44

86

Fig.41 Coconut palm (Cocos nucifera).

Fig.42 Rambutan (Nephelium lappaceum L.).

Fig.43 Cacao (Theobroma cacao L.).

Fig.44 Carolina moth with fruit resembling custard apple.

45

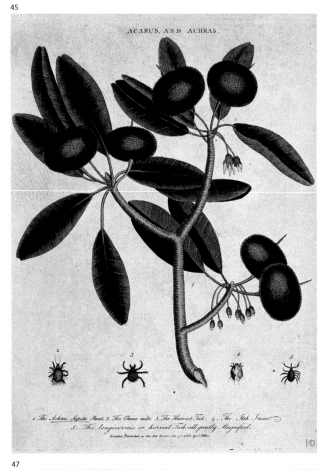

46

47

48

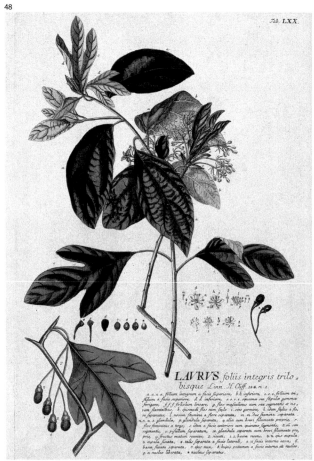

Fig.45 Sapodillo tree (Manilkara zapota) and four mites.

Fig.46 Duroia eriophila.

Fig.47 Huru and bull bay (Magnolia grandiflora L.).

Fig.48 Laurus.

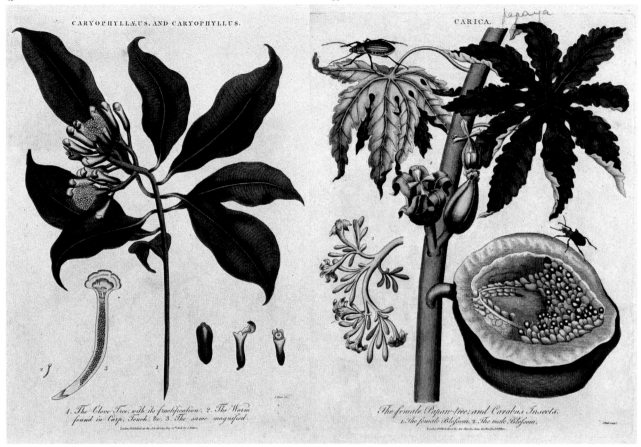

CARYOPHYLLÆUS, AND CARYOPHYLLUS.

CARICA. *papaya*

1. The Clove Tree, with its fructification. 2. The Worm
found in Carp. Tench. &c. 3. The same magnified.

The female Papaw-tree; and Carabus Insects.
1. The female Blossom. 2. The male Blossom.

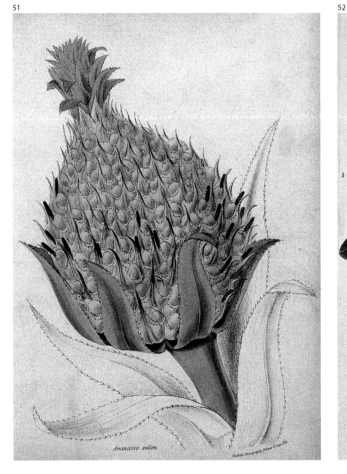

Ananassa sativa.

The Ickworth Imperatrice Plum.

Fig.49 Clove tree (Syzygium
aromaticum).

Fig.50 Papaw or papaya (Carica
papaya).

Fig.51 Pineapple (Ananas
comosus).

Fig.52 The Ickworth Imperatrice
plum .

VINTAGE BOTANICAL ILLUSTRATION

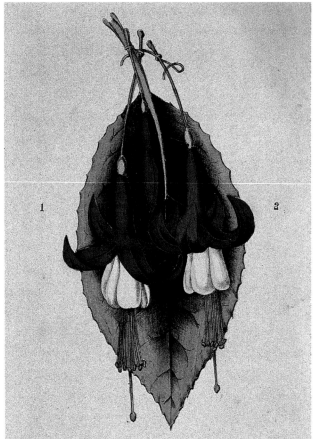

55

56

Fig.53 Certostema longiflorum.

Fig.54 Two cultivars of fuchsia.

Fig.55 A double-flowered
geranium.

Fig.56 Orange and white lily
flowers.

57

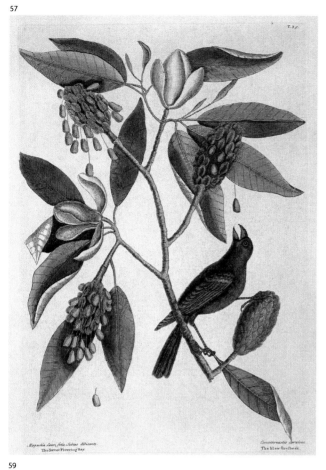

58

Epacris densiflora.
(Serre, frondé)

59

60

Fig.57 Blue cross-beak and
Sweet flowering bay.

Fig.58 Epacris denisflora.

Fig.59 An indigo plant (Indigo-
fera stachyoides).

Fig.60 A begonia plant (Begonia
crassicaulis).

VINTAGE BOTANICAL ILLUSTRATION

61

62

63

64

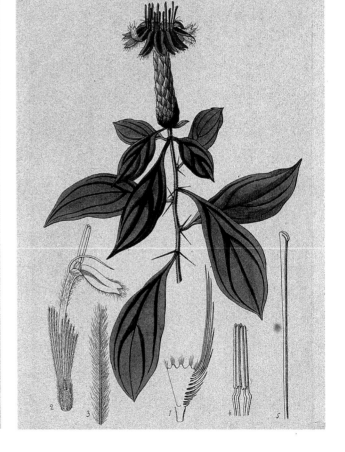

Fig.61 Stenomesson humile.

Fig.62 A tropical orchid (Bulbo-
phyllum species).

Fig.63 A tropical orchid (Coelia
baueriana).

Fig.64 A tropical plant (Barnade-
sia rosea).

Point d'après nature par M.me Berthe Hoola van Nooten, à Batavia.

Chromolith. par P. Depannemacker, à Ledeberg-lez-Gand. (Belgique)

CYNOMETRA CAULIFLORA. L.

Librairie C. Muquardt, éditeur, Bruxelles.

Fig.65 A plant (Cynometra
cauliflora L.).

66

67

68

69

Fig.66 Philesia buxifolia.

Fig.67 A plant (Tillandsia musaica), after S. Drake.

Fig.68 Tall Limodorum.

Fig.69 Episcia.

FUCHSIA AND FULGORA.

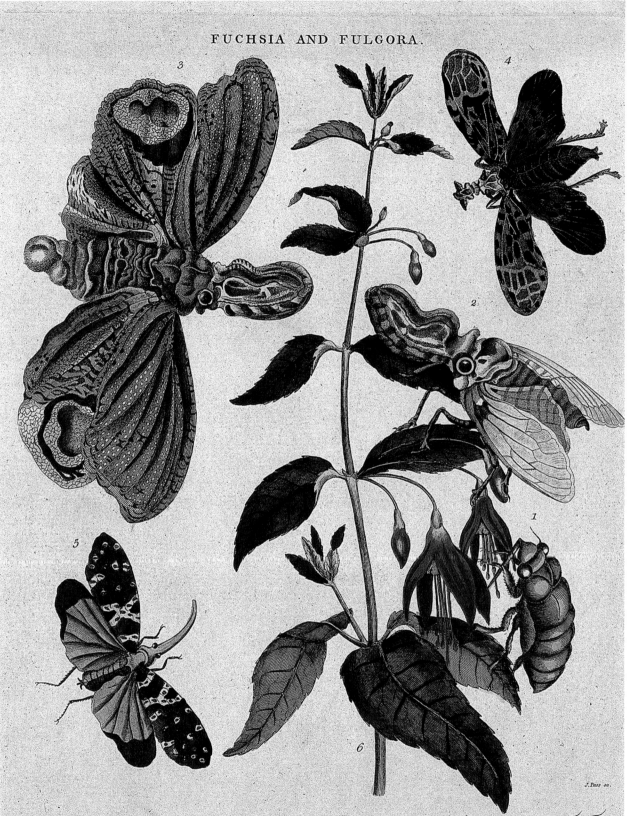

1. The Lanthorn Fly in its pupa state. 2. The same about half evolved. 3. Its mature state. 4. The Fulgora diadema. 5. The Fulgora Candelaria. 6. The Fuchia coccinea Plant.

London, Published as the Act directs, Nov.r s.? 1805, by J. Wilkes.

Fig.70 A flowering fuchsia (Fuchsia coccinea).

71

72

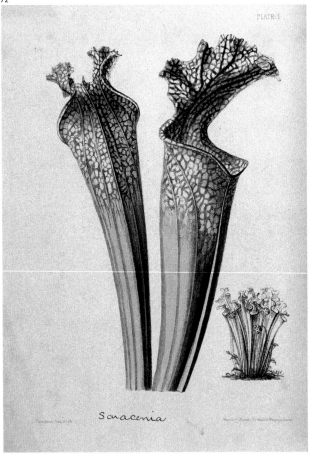

73

Fig.71 Clematus pateus.

Fig.72 A pitcher plant (Sarrace-
nia drummondii).

Fig.73 A pitcher plant (Sarrace-
nia drummondii).

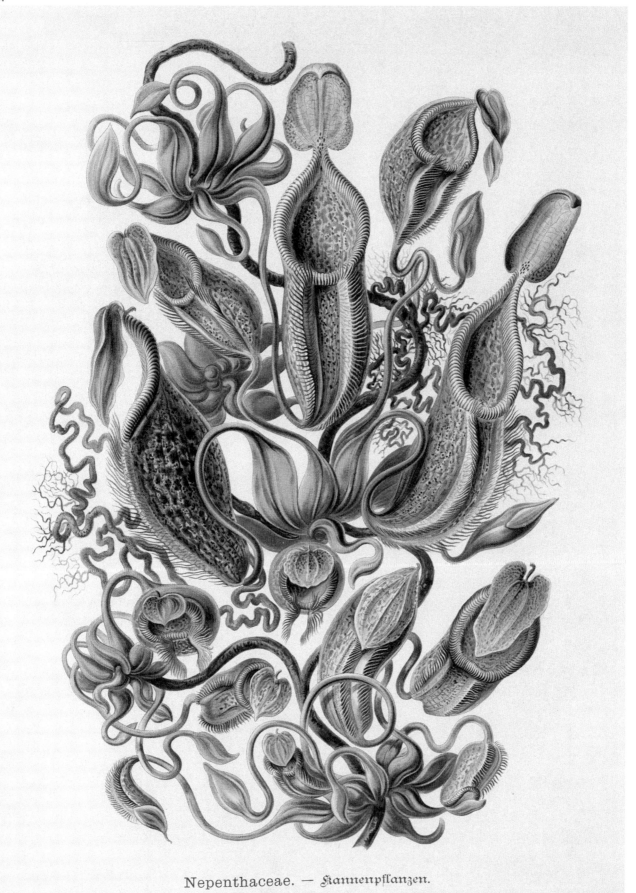

Nepenthaceae. — Kannenpflanzen.

Fig.74 Nepenthaceae.

THE "DOUBLE" POINSETTIA P. PULCHERRIMA PLENISSIMA. (Half the natural size)

76

DAHLIA—DR. FRAMPTON.

77

PELARGONIUM
(The Baron)

Fig.75 A double flowered poinsettia (Euphorbia pulcherrima).

Fig.76 A dahlia (Dahlia species).

Fig.77 Pelargonium plant (Pelargonium T he Baron').

Peint d'après nature par Mme Berthe Hoola van Nooten, à Batavia.   Chromolith. par P. Depannemaeker, à Ledeberg-lez-Gand. (Belgique).

AMARANTUS TRICOLOR. L. BAYEM MEERA.

Librairie C. Muquardt, éditeur, Bruxelles.

Fig.78 Joseph's Coat (Amaranthus tricolor L.).

VINTAGE BOTANICAL ILLUSTRATION

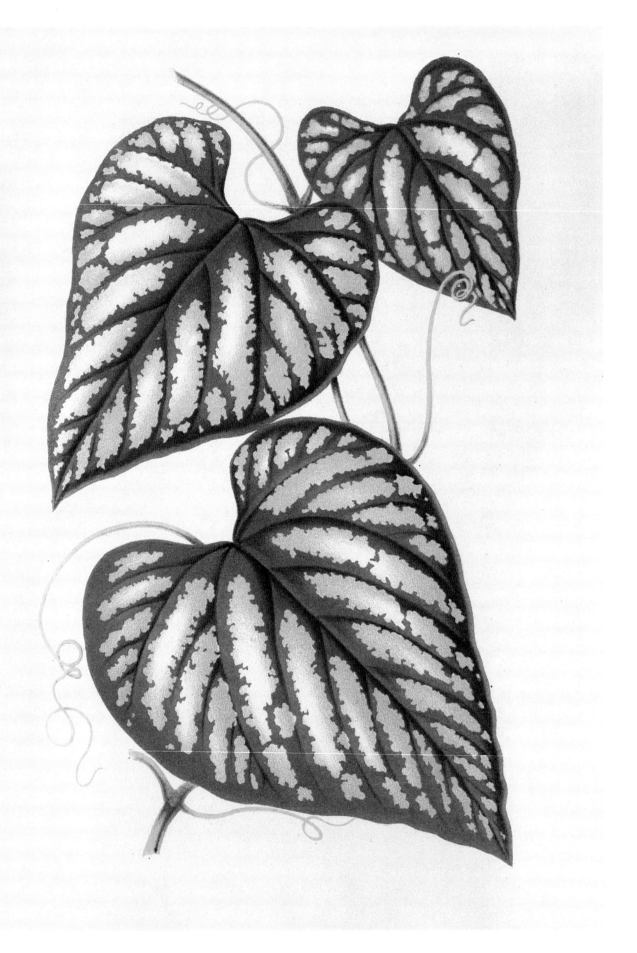

Fig.79 Cissus lindeni.

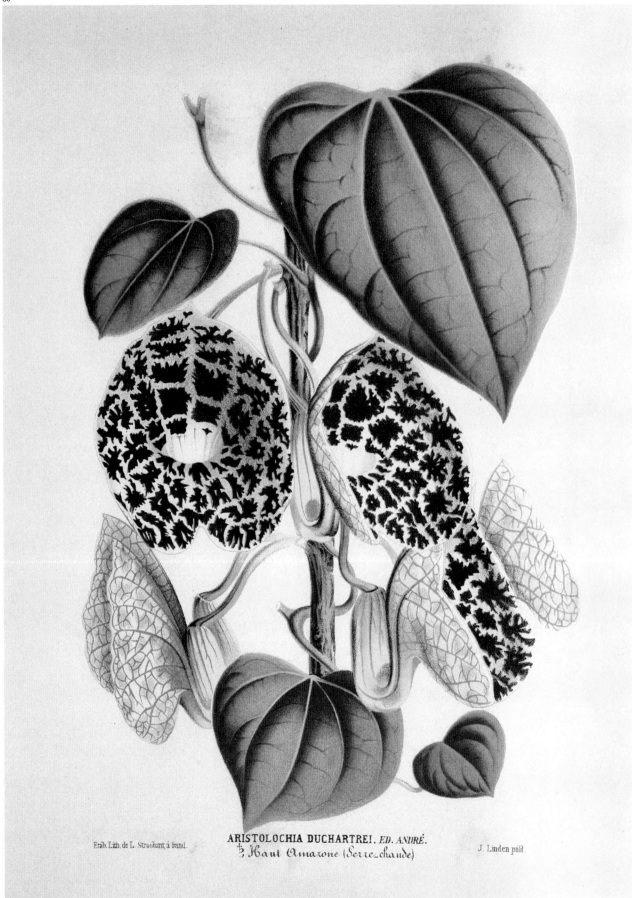

ARISTOLOCHIA DUCHARTREI. *ED. ANDRÉ.*

Haut Amazone (Serre-chaude)

Etab. Lith. de L. Stroobant, à Gand.

J. Linden publ.

Fig.80 Aristolochia duchartrei.

VINTAGE BOTANICAL ILLUSTRATION

HORT. TRANS. Vol.II, SECOND SERIES. Pl.5.

Oncidium Lanceanum.

Drake, del.

169

Fig.81 A tropical orchid (Oncidium lanceanum).

Orchideae. — Venusblumen.

Fig.82 Orchids, Various.

VINTAGE BOTANICAL ILLUSTRATION

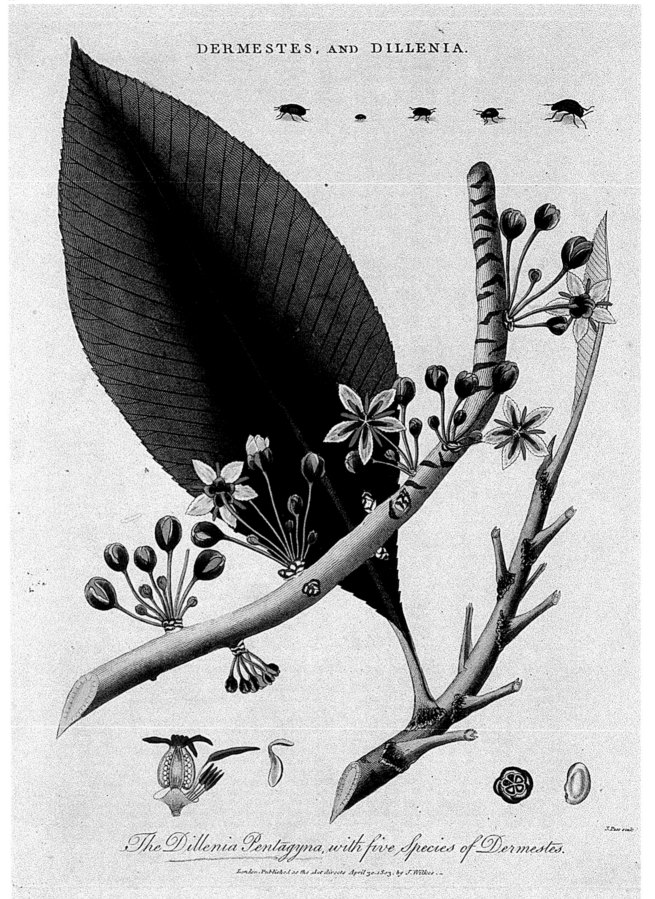

DERMESTES, AND DILLENIA.

The Dillenia Pentagyna, with five Species of Dermestes.

London. Published as the Act directs April 30.1803. by J.Wilkes.

Fig.83 Dillenia pentagyna.

84

PYRETHRUM SOUVENIR DE VANDERVINNEN.
Serms. Bruxelles (Plein air)

85

CLUSIA.

The Rose coloured Balsam Tree.

27

86

BLANDFORDIA CUNNINGHAMI. Lindl.
Nouvelle Galles du sud. (Serre froide)

87

W.G.Smith, F.L.S. del et lith..

V.Brooks, Day & Son, Imp.

TOXICOPHLÆA SPECTABILIS

FLORAL MAGAZINE. NEW SERIES.

L. Reeve & Co.5, Henrietta St. Covent Garden.

1872

Fig.84 Pyrethrum.

Fig.85 Rock balsam plant (Clusia rosea).

Fig.86 Blandfordia cunninghami.

Fig.87 A tropical plant (Acokanthera spectabilis).

SARACA DECLINATA. Miq.

ANONA RETICULATA L.

SYZYGIUM JAMBOLANUM DC.

ANONA SQUAMOSA. L.

VINTAGE BOTANICAL ILLUSTRATION

Fig.88 Saraca declinata Miq.

Fig.89 Custard apple or Bullock's heart (Annona reticulata L.).

Fig.90 Jambolan or Java plum (Eugenia jambolana Lam.).

Fig.91 Custard apple or Sweetsop (Annona squamosa L.).

92

LILIUM FORMOSUM. (♀♀♀)

93

94

COCCOLOBO.

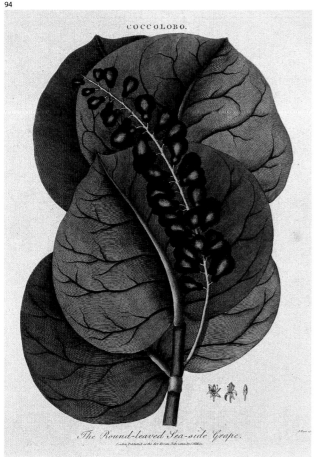

The Round-leaved Sea-side Grape.

95

TACSONIA BUCHANANI. Hort. New-York.
Panama (serre chaude).

Fig.92 Lilium Formosum.

Fig.93 Brucea species.

Fig.94 Seaside grape (Coccoloba uvifera).

Fig.95 Tacsonia Buchanani.

COCCINELLA, AND COCCUS.

Fig.1.to 15. different Species of Coccinella. Fig.16.to 21. male and female Coccus. Fig.22.to 27. the Insect supposed to feed on the Coccus.

BOTANY.

Plate III.

The different Kinds of Trunks and Stems. No 2.

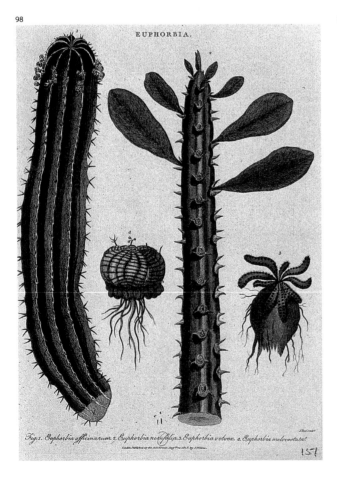

EUPHORBIA.

Fig.1. Euphorbia officinarum. 2. Euphorbia neriifolia. 3. Euphorbia volvox. 4. Euphorbia melocostata.

CACTUS.

Plate I.

The great Echinated Melon thistle or Turk's Cap.

78

C melocactus

VINTAGE BOTANICAL ILLUSTRATION

Fig.96 Cochineal cactus (Nopalea cochenillifera).

Fig.97 Fourteen different forms of plant stem.

Fig.98 Four types of spurge (Euphorbia species).

Fig.99 Turk's cap cactus (Melocactus communis).

100

101

102

103

Fig.100 Astiophytum
Myriostigma.

Fig.101 Eight plants, including an
orchid, a magnolia and a cactus.

Fig.102 Seven plants, including
two orchids and a cactus.

Fig.103 A prickly pear (Opuntia
species).

104

105

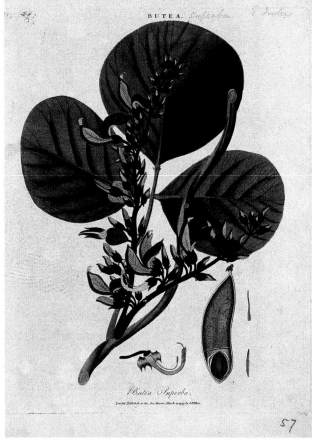

106

107

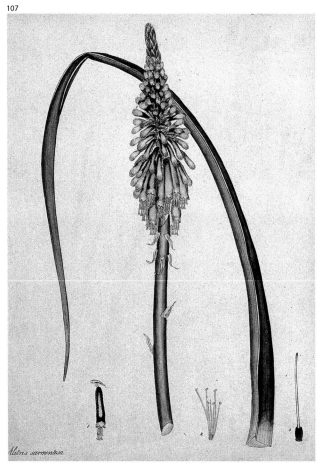

Fig.104 Azalea Indica.

Fig.105 Dhak or palas tree (Butea monosperma).

Fig.106 Citron (Citrus medica).

Fig.107 A torch lily (Kniphofia alooides).

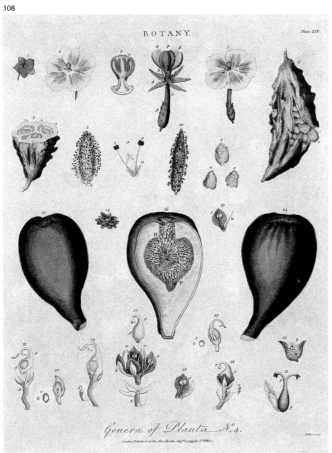

Fig.108 Genera of plants No.4.

Fig.109 Pomme Calville Garibaldi.

Fig.110 A branch of a Prunus cultivar.

Fig.111 A houseleek (Sempervivum arachnoideum).

VINTAGE BOTANICAL ILLUSTRATION

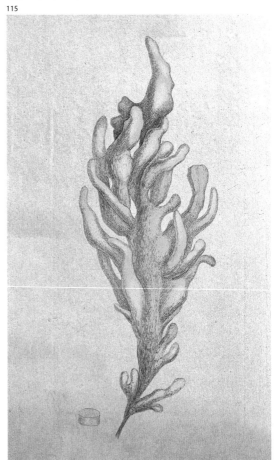

Fig.112 Coffee plant (Coffea arabica).

Fig.113 A yellow iris (Iris variegata).

Fig.114 A plant (Amaranthus cruentus).

Fig.115 A green algae (Ulva diaphana).

116

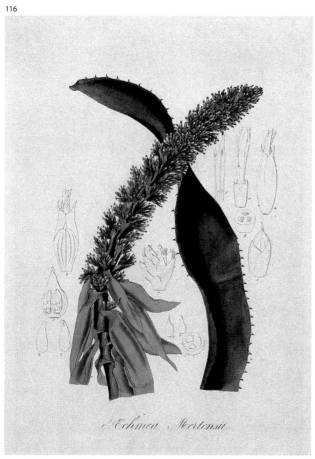

117

Epacris multiflora BOT. REG.

118

119

SANCHEZIA NOBILIS. J. D. Hook.

Fig.116 A tropical plant
(Aechmea mertensii).

Fig.117 Epacris Multiflora.

Fig.118 A tropical plant (Meme-
cylon edule).

Fig.119 Sanchezia Nobilis.

VINTAGE BOTANICAL ILLUSTRATION

Petunia inimitabilis flore pleno.

Compositae.

Inula Helenium. L.

Clianthus puniceus.

Fig.120 Plumeria tree.

Fig.121 Petunia Inimitabilis, Flore Pleno.

Fig.122 Elecampane plant (Inula helenium).

Fig.123 Glory pea (Clianthus puniceus).

Fig.124 Camphor tree (Cinnamo-mum camphora).

Fig.125 Cuckoo-pint (Arum maculatum).

Fig.126 A lady's slipper orchid (Cypripedium x schroederae).

Fig.127 Coleus plant (Solenoste-mon scutellarioides).

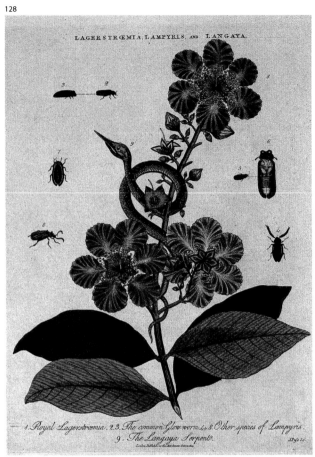

LAGERSTROEMIA, LAMPYRIS, AND LANGAYA.

1. *Royal Lagerstroemia.* 2.3. *The common Glow worm.* 4.v.8. *Other species of Lampyris.*
9. *The Langaya Serpent.*

MAGNOLIA: *Altissima LAURO-CERASSI Folia flore ingenti candido, caug Commonly call'd the LAUREL-LEAUE'D TULIP TREE or Carolina Laurel.*

EXPLANATION

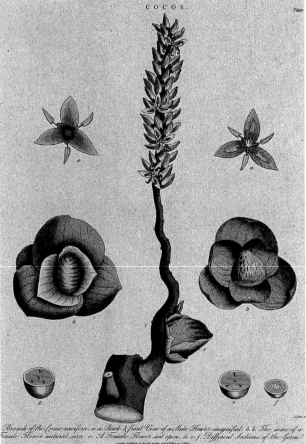

COCOS.

Branch of the Cocoa nucifera. a.a. Back & front View of a Male Flower magnified. b.b. The same of a Female Flower natural size. c. A Female Flower not open. d.e.f. Different Sections of the Germ.

Iris Florentina.

Fig.128 A flowering queen-flower (Lagerstroemia speciosa).

Fig.129 A Magnolia species.

Fig.130 Coconut palm (Cocos nucifera).

Fig.131 Flag iris.

Aristolochia hyperborea.

Fig.132 Aristolochia hyperborea.

133

134

135

Fig.133 A lady's slipper orchid
(Cypripedium sallieri).

Fig.134 An orchid (Dendrobium
moschatum).

Fig.135 An orchid (Catasetum
bungerothi N.E.Brown).

Fig.136 A tropical orchid (Aganisia cyanea).

Fig.137 A tropical orchid (Miltonia spectabilis var. Moreliana).

Fig.138 Amygdalus Rosaeflora.

Fig.139 A butterfly orchid (Oncidium barkerii).

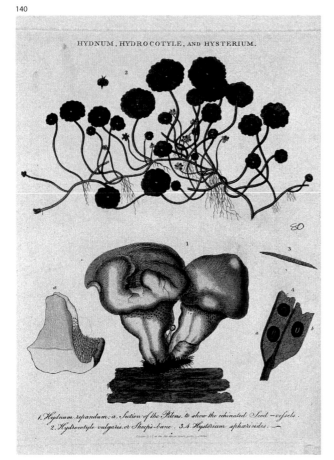

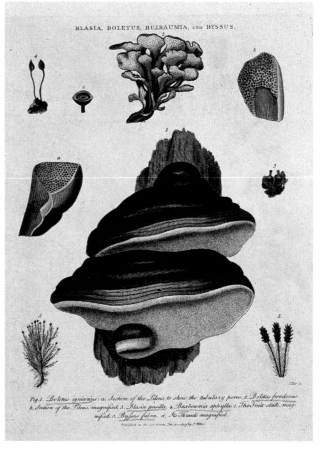

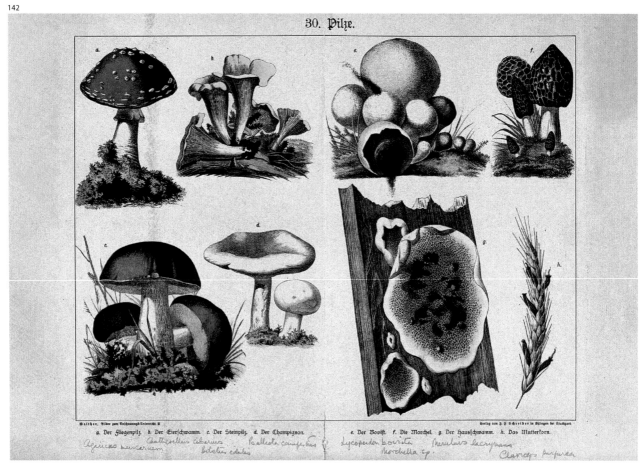

VINTAGE BOTANICAL ILLUSTRATION

Fig.140 Wood hedgehog fungus (Hydnum repandum).

Fig.141 Five fungi.

Fig.142 Eight fungi, including the fly agaric.

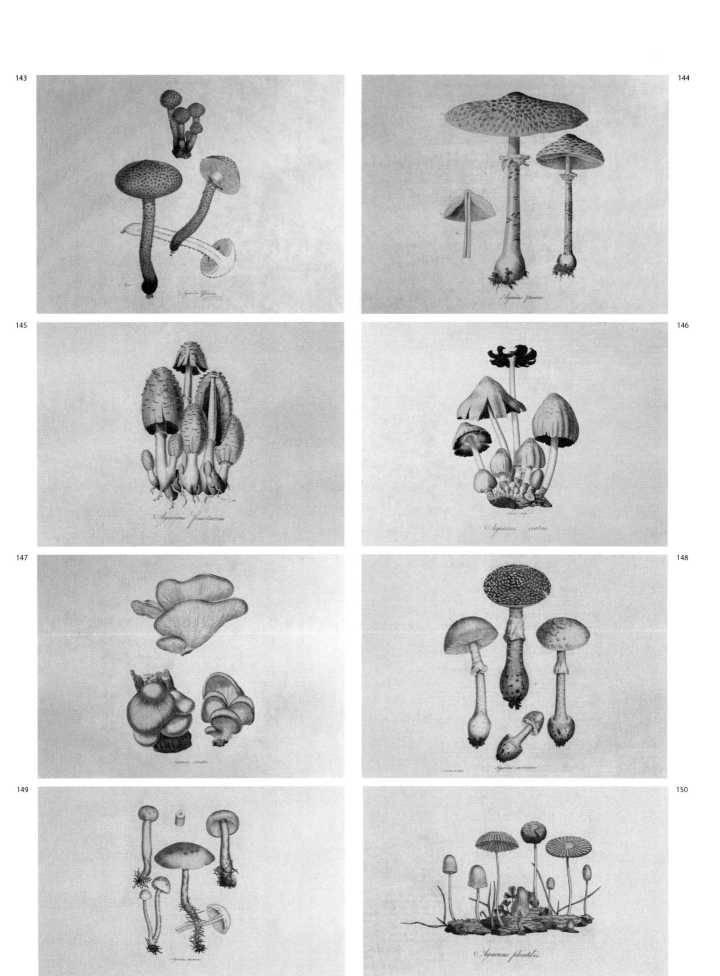

143

144

145

146

147

148

149

150

Fig.143-150 Various fungi.

VINTAGE BOTANICAL ILLUSTRATION

151

152

153

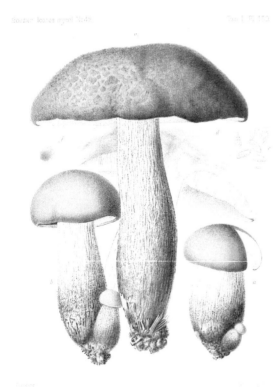

154

Fig.151 Scleroderma Geaster.   Fig.152 Lycoperdon Bovista.   Fig.153 Boletus Duriusculus.   Fig.154 Polyprus Giganteus.

Fig.155 Clitocybe Tabescens.   Fig.156 Cortinarius Torvus.   Fig.157 Psalliota Elvensis.   Fig.158 Lentinus Variabilis.

159

160

161

162

Fig.159 Pitchradia Pacifica.

Fig.160 Anthurium Floribundum.

Fig.161 Clidemia Vittata.

Fig.162 Dracaena Bellula.

Fig.163 Oncidium Sarcodes.   Fig.164 Cortinarius Torvus.   Fig.165 Psalliota Elvensis.   Fig.166 Croton Hastiferum.

167

168

169

170

Fig.167 Dracaena Warocquei.   Fig.168 Clidemia Vittata.   Fig.169 Centrosolenia Aenea.   Fig.170 Cocos Weddelliana.

CROTON (CODIÆUM) BELLULUM, Linden & André.

(Grandeur naturelle.)

DICKSONIA CHRYSOTRICHA, Moore.

Fig.171 Astrocaryum Murumuru.   Fig.172 Croton Bellulum.   Fig.173 Dicksonia Chrysotricha.

TRITHRINAX BRASILIENSIS, Martius.

176

177

Fig.174 Trithrinax Brasiliensis.

Fig.175 Masdevallia Amabilis.

Fig.176 Zamia Lindeni.

Fig.177 Dieffenbachia Antio-
quensis.

Fig.178 Thrinax Barbadensis.   Fig.179 Kentia Balmoreana.   Fig.180 Tillandsia Tessellata.   Fig.181 Dracaena Troubetzkoi.

VINTAGE BOTANICAL ILLUSTRATION

Fig.182 Bonnbergia Morreniana.

Fig.183 Vriesea Sanguinolenta.

Fig.184 Spathiphyllum Helico-
niaefolium.

Fig.185 Clavija Rodekiana.

Fig.186 Cypriedium Parishii.

Fig.187 Camellia Don Pedro.

Fig.188 Lasiandra Lepidota.

Fig.189 Aphelandra Fascinator.

190

191

192

193

Fig.190 Epidendrum Panicu-
latum.

Fig.191 Orchid.

Fig.192 Epidendrum Catillus.

Fig.193 Ocnidium Tigrinum.

Fig.194 Camellia Albino Botti.　　　　Fig.195 Camellia.　　　　Fig.196 Orchid.　　　　Fig.197 Azalea Madame Gloner.

VINTAGE BOTANICAL ILLUSTRATION

Fig.198 Azalea.

Fig.199 Orchid.

Fig.200 Orchid.

Fig.201 Azalea.

202

203

204

205

Fig.202 Orchid.　　　　　Fig.203 Orchid.　　　　　Fig.204 Sciadocalyx Luciani.　　　　　Fig.205 Camellia.

VINTAGE BOTANICAL ILLUSTRATION

Fig.206 Azalea Indica.

Fig.207 Dendrobium
Thyrsiflorum.

Fig.208 Rheum Nobile.

Fig.209 Araucaria
Balansae.

Fig.210 Ceroxylon Andicola.

Fig.211 Pêcher feuilles Pourpres (Peach).

Fig.212 Cinchona plant (Cinchona officinalis).

Fig.213 Cinchona plant (Cinchona officinalis).

VINTAGE BOTANICAL ILLUSTRATION

214

AZALEA INDICA FRANÇOIS DEVOS (A Versch.)
Semis Gand. (Serre froide.)

215

Azalea indica Bealii.
Chine. (Serre froide.)

216

CAMELLIA CONSTANTIN TRETIAKOFF.
Hort. A. Versch. (Serre froide.)

217

CAMELLIA ROMA RISORTA (Bel. Gratiom.)
Serre froide.

Fig.214 Azalea Indica
Francois Devos.

Fig.215 Azalea Indica
Bealu.

Fig.216 Camellia
Constantin Tretiakoff.

Fig.217 Camellia Roma
Risorta.

CAMELLIA CLODIA *(Hort.)*
Semis - Italie. (Serre froide.)

Fig.218 A camellia clodia.

VINTAGE BOTANICAL ILLUSTRATION

CAMELLIA MARIANNA TALENTI.
Semis Italie (Serre froide)
A. Verschaffelt, publ.

CAMELLIA STELLA POLARE
Semis Italie (Serre froide).
A. Verschaffelt, publ.

WEIGELIA (MIDDEND.) Var PURPURATA.
Semis Hollande, Plein air.
A. Verschaffelt, publ.

LOBELIA CORONOPIFOLIA. L.
Caffirie (Serre froide.)

Fig.219 Camellia
marianna talenti.

Fig.220 Camellia stella
polare.

Fig.221 Weigelia
(middend) Var Purpurata.

Fig.222 Lobelia
Coronopifolia.

223

224

225

226

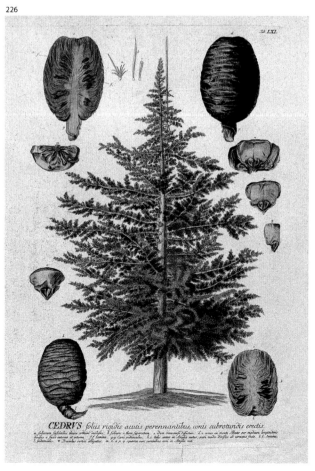

Fig.223 The century plant (Agave americana).

Fig.224 Barbados aloe plant (Aloe vera).

Fig.225 Cedar (Cedrus sp.).

Fig.226 Cedar (Cedrus sp.).

227

228

VINTAGE BOTANICAL ILLUSTRATION

229

230

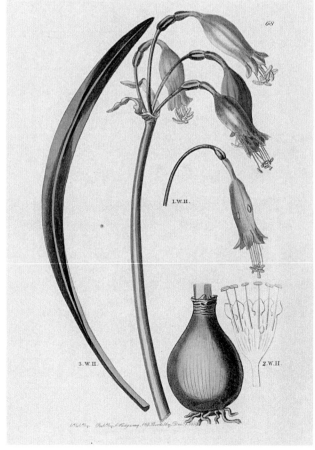

Fig.227 -231 Collection
from Edwards's Ornamen-
tal Flower-Garden.

Miss Drake del.   Pub. by J. Ridgway 169 Piccadilly Aug 1 1839   G Barclay sc.

4.

VINTAGE BOTANICAL ILLUSTRATION

Fig.232 -236 Collection
from Edwards's Ornamen-
tal Flower-Garden.

233

234

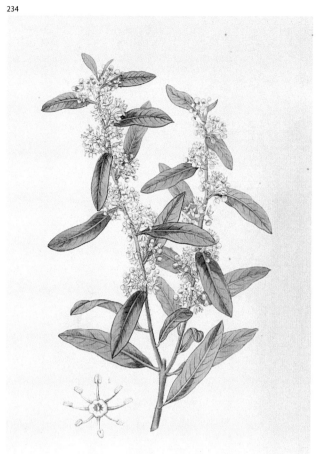

235

236

237

238

239

VINTAGE BOTANICAL ILLUSTRATION

Fig.237-240 Collection
from Edwards's Ornamen-
tal Flower-Garden.

VINTAGE BOTANICAL ILLUSTRATION

Fig.241 -245 Collection
from Edwards's Ornamen-
tal Flower-Garden.

246

247

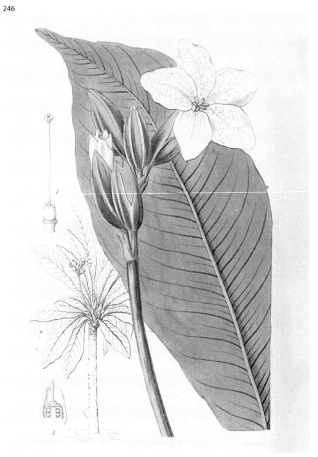

248

249

Fig.246 -250 Collection
from Edwards's Ornamen-
tal Flower-Garden.

Fig.251 -255 Collection
from Edwards's Ornamen-
tal Flower-Garden.

256

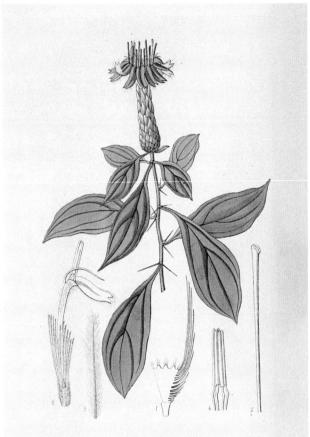

257

258

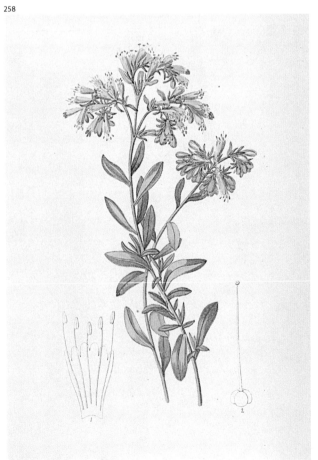

259

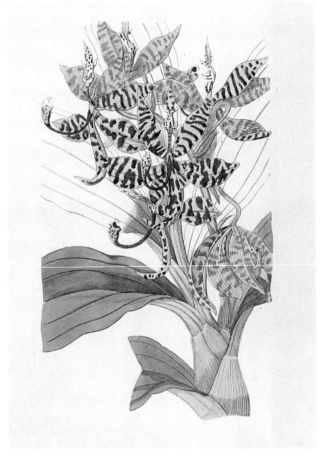

VINTAGE BOTANICAL ILLUSTRATION

Fig.256 -260 Collection
from Edwards's Ornamen-
tal Flower-Garden.

VINTAGE BOTANICAL ILLUSTRATION

Fig.261 -265 Collection
from Edwards's Ornamen-
tal Flower-Garden.

262

263

264

265

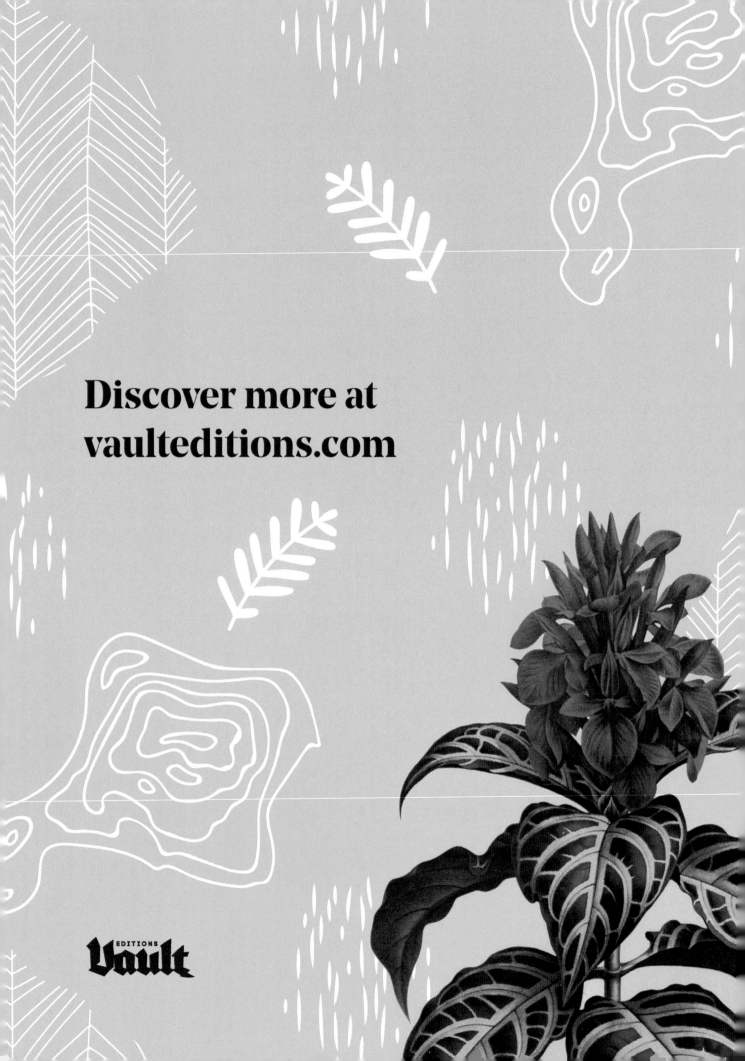

Discover more at
vaulteditions.com

EDITIONS Vault

Made in the USA
Coppell, TX
22 August 2023

20663529R00055